Enjoy your
learning Ra.
Fayola

# REBELS FOR FREEDOM ACTIVITY BOOK

Suitable for KS1, KS2 and KS3.

Drawing upon information from the Rebels for Freedom children's book. Filled with lots of fun and challenging activities and can be used in the classroom and at home. Tips and answers at the back.

# TASK 1 – READING GROUP DISCUSSION QUESTIONS

1. Why is it important to learn about Black history?

2. Which slaves have you heard of before?

3. How do you celebrate Black History Month?

4. What is an abolitionist?

5. What do you know about Africa and the Caribbean?

# TASK 2 – WHERE DID THE REBELLIONS TAKE PLACE? LABEL THE MAP BELOW WITH AN X.

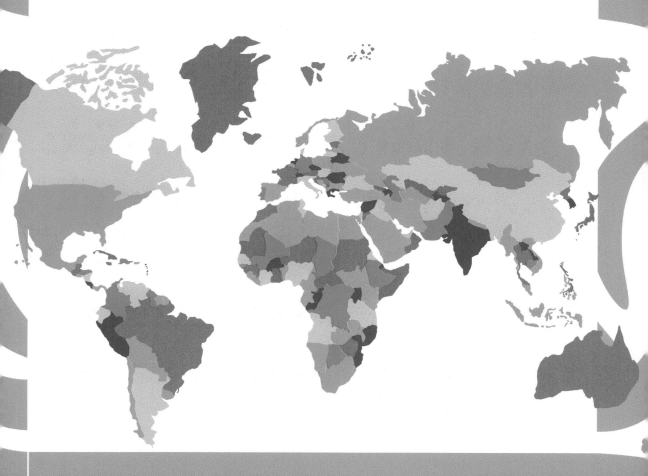

# TASK 3 – CHOOSE ONE OF THE REBELS FROM THE BOOK. WRITE A DIARY ENTRY BASED ON THEIR FEELINGS.

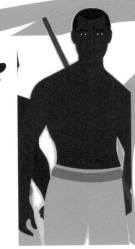

DEAR DIARY,

# TASK 4 - GET THE ENSLAVED REBEL TO THE MAROON COMMUNITY IN THE MOUNTAINS SAFELY.

# TASK 5 – COMPLETE THE CROSSWORD

Use the clues below!

## Across

**2.** Name for era when blacks were of high social status

**4.** Surname of father and son duo involved in Demerara Rebellion

**7.** Female that led Akamu revolt

**8.** Treaty used to end war

**10.** People who helped to educate slaves

## Down

**1.** Free people and runaway slaves developed communities here

**3.** Statue in Barbados named after this rebel

**5.** The month the Akamu rebellion took place

**6.** This man is responsible for the Haitian Revolution

**9.** A film was named after this rebellion

# TASK 6 – COMPLETE THE WORDSEARCH

```
D  N  H  C  A  M  E  Y  T  A  L  U  D  G  R
U  Q  C  R  E  O  L  E  S  O  L  O  R  U  Q
J  H  B  C  L  B  E  R  B  I  C  E  A  Y  B
V  G  P  X  E  Z  T  N  X  S  V  G  P  A  U
U  Z  E  B  M  A  R  O  O  N  T  L  E  N  S
B  N  F  Z  G  F  E  M  U  K  O  G  T  A  S
W  Q  R  U  L  L  B  S  J  U  K  D  O  E  A
A  T  W  L  Z  M  E  K  H  B  Q  P  M  A  V
Q  U  L  K  Y  Z  L  V  T  A  F  W  A  G  D
J  E  G  Y  W  I  L  I  F  R  R  G  N  F  E
N  H  K  X  U  S  I  R  N  B  E  Y  I  I  M
P  O  J  O  M  U  O  N  H  A  T  N  A  P  A
H  A  I  T  I  T  N  F  Z  D  F  X  P  T  R
M  I  H  K  K  A  P  L  W  O  J  C  T  O  A
R  A  I  P  S  W  P  M  R  S  G  X  Z  C  J
```

drapetomania          rebellion          barbados          haiti

berbice               guyana             creole

maroon                demara             bussa

# TASK 8 - COLOURING IN

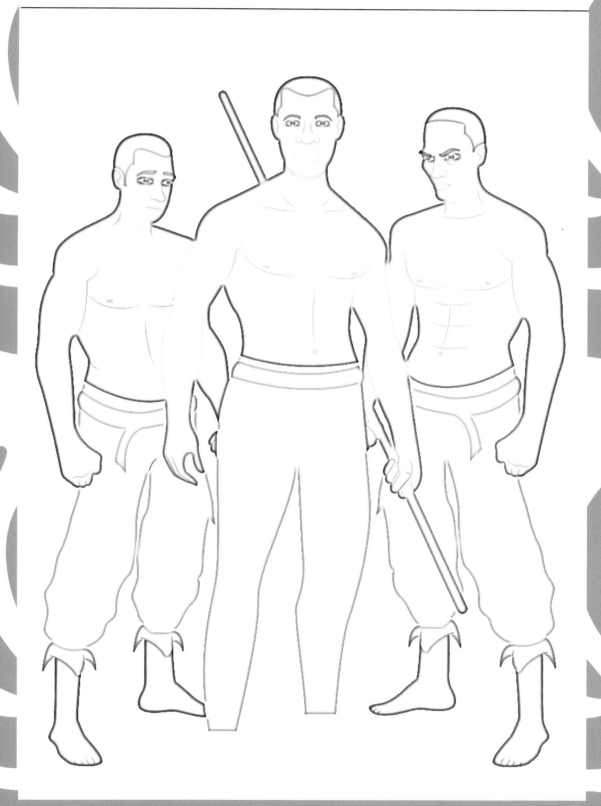

# TASK 9 – COMPLETE THE SENTENCES BY FILLING IN THE GAPS. USE THE WORDS TO HELP.

SLAVERY WAS ABOLISHED IN THE UK IN _____.
IT WAS ABOLISHED IN THE _____ IN 1865.
SLAVERY WAS MADE _____ BECAUSE OF
THE EFFORTS OF _____ PEOPLE.
IT WAS ALSO ABOLISHED DUE TO WHITE
ABOLITIONISTS SUCH AS

_____

_____.

_____ WAS THE
FIRST NATION TO
BAN SLAVERY.

HAITI

ILLEGAL

ABRAHAM
LINCOLN

USA

ENSLAVED

1807

# TASK 10 – CHOOSE A REBELLION. CREATE A COMIC BOOK STRIP ABOUT THE PEOPLE INVOLVED.

# TASK 11 – TALKING HEADS. WRITE SOME THOUGHTS FROM EACH PERSON.

# TASK 12 – ANAGRAM SOLVER – WHAT ARE THE REAL NAMES OF THE REBELS?

ANN RUTTER

AME SHARPS

JECHO QUINN

BUFFER

ANITRA HUMBERT

ROMONAS

# TASK 13 – CAN YOU SPOT THE MISTAKES IN THE TEXT?

Maroon rebelon
Location: Jamaica/guyana

After being enslaved by European colonists, many slaves escaped to mountains. Three communities developed in the moutains and those that tried to recapture them were attacked.

Mistakes:

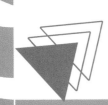

# TASK 14 – CREATE A TIMELINE OF THE REBELLIONS IN THE BOOK FROM BEGINNING TO END

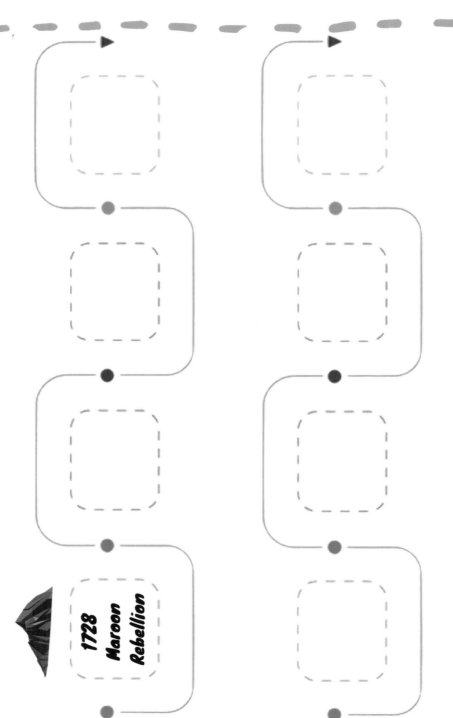

1728
Maroon
Rebellion

# TASK 1

Tips -
Teachers and parents/guardians. Explore the front and back pages of the Rebels for Freedom children's book whilst discussing these questions. Draw upon previous learning, such as history and non fiction texts to widen discussion

# TASK 3

**QUICK TIPS** Tips - teachers and parentsguardians

Diary entries should include dates, what happened on that day and feelings of person writing the entry. Have a read of the Rebels for Freedom children's book to get some ideas about what to include.

# TASK 4

# TASK 5

## Across

2 - Jacobin

4 - Gladstone

7 - Beffru

8 - Peace

10 - Missionaries

## Down

1 - Mountain

3 - Bussa

5 - November

6 - Toussaint

9 - Amistad

# TASK 6

D N H C A M E Y T A L U D G R
U Q C R E O L E S O L O R U Q
J H B C L B E R B I C E A Y B
V G P X E Z T N X S V G P A U
U Z E B M A R O O N T L E N S
B N F Z G F E M U K O G T A S
W Q R U L L B S J U K D O E A
A T W L Z M E K H B Q P M A V
Q U L K Y Z L V T A F W A G D
J E G Y W I L I F R R G N F E
N H K X U S I R N B E Y I I M
P O J O M U O N H A T N A P A
H A I T I T N F Z D F X P T R
M I H K K A P L W O J C T O A
R A I P S W P M R S G X Z C J

drapetomania       rebellion        barbados        haiti

berbice            guyana           creole

maroon             demara           bussa

SLAVERY WAS ABOLISHED IN THE UK IN 1807.
IT WAS ABOLISHED IN THE USA IN 1865.
SLAVERY WAS MADE ILLEGAL BECAUSE OF THE EFFORTS OF ENSLAVED PEOPLE.
IT WAS ALSO ABOLISHED DUE TO WHITE ABOLITIONISTS SUCH AS ABRAHAM LINCOLN.
HAITI WAS THE FIRST NATION TO BAN SLAVERY.

# TASK 12

NAT TURNER

SAM SHARPE

JOHN CINQUE

BEFFRU

HARRIET TUBMAN

MAROONS

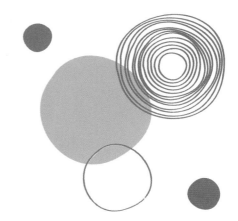

# TASK 13

Maroon rebellion
Location: Jamaica/Guyana

After being enslaved by European colonists, many slaves escaped to mountains. Free communities developed in the mountains and those that tried to recapture them were attacked.

Published by FMW
Publishing Ltd
July 2023

Printed in Great Britain
by Amazon